Yes! I Can

Make A Difference

First published in Great Britain in 2001 by
Go MAD Books
Pocket Gate Farm
Off Breakback Road
Woodhouse Eaves
Leicestershire
LE12 8RS

British Library Cataloguing in Publication Data.
A catalogue record for this book is available from the
British Library.

ISBN 0-9537284-7-1

Printed and bound in Great Britain by
Cox & Wyman, Reading

INTRODUCTION

Welcome to your book. The chances are that it happens to be in your possession through one of the following ways:

- You bought it, with the intention of writing in it.

- You received it as a gift from a friend - maybe someone who has heard you say, "One day I am going to write a book."

- You received it as part of a Go MAD® Development Programme.

Now that this book is yours, there are a couple of essential things to do. Firstly, if you haven't done so already, write your name on the front cover. Now it really is *your* book. The next, and most important, thing to do is to decide what to write in your book. However, before you make your decision let me explain some of the background about Go MAD® and how this book came into existence.

Where it all began

Several years ago I became fascinated by the whole subject of "making a difference," particularly how to achieve success on a consistent basis. So, over a 14 month period, I led a major research study to identify the key success principles that need to be applied in order to make a difference.

The research involved hundreds of interviews with interesting people who had each made a worthwhile difference to some aspect of their life. These encompassed big and small differences in a wide variety of areas including business, social, career, family, community and education. The research team listened to hours of interview recordings and studied video footage of the interviews. From all of this information emerged Go MAD® – a simple, yet sophisticated, development process to help people achieve results and make a difference in their personal and professional lives.

At its simplest, Go MAD® is an easy to understand set of seven key principles. At a more complex level, Go MAD® links these principles together to form a framework which explains the natural process we all use to make a difference.

The seven key principles

1. Have a strong reason why you want to Go MAD®
2. Define your goal before starting to Go MAD®
3. Plan priorities before taking action to Go MAD®
4. Develop self-belief that you will Go MAD®
5. Involve others to Go MAD®

6. Take personal responsibility for your actions
7. Take action and measure results

Principle 1 considers WHY you want to make a difference.
Principle 2 focuses on WHAT difference you want to make.
Principles 3 - 7 concentrate on HOW to make a difference.

Developing the ability to make a difference

It is perhaps easiest to think of Go MAD® as an ability that can be further developed. As a competency it encompasses the following areas:

- self-motivation
- goal defining
- use of imagination
- problem solving
- risk assessment
- prioritisation
- project planning
- time management
- personal development planning
- building effective relationships
- measuring results
- resource analysis
- self-awareness
- creative thinking
- team working
- communication
- influencing skills
- leadership
- decision making
- personal responsibility
- thinking strategies

The research we conducted identified how all these areas not only contributed to making a difference, but actually fitted together into a process with universal applicability. In essence, we pieced together the "D.N.A." pattern of how to make a measurable difference.

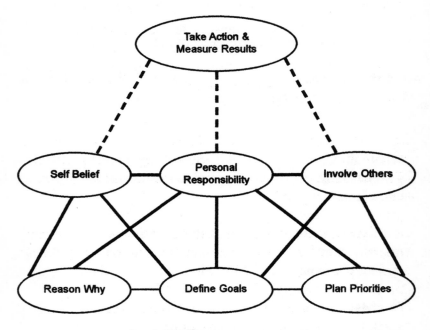

Go MAD® - The Framework

Once these links and the relationships between them are clearly understood, and the relevant skills are developed, then Go MAD® can be consciously applied as a process to any situation in order to make a difference and achieve results.

How is Go MAD® used as a process?

Go MAD® can be used as a development process to achieve results in the following ways:

- A coaching framework to help individuals make a difference.
- A facilitation framework for business meetings.
- A project planning framework for teams.
- A competency framework for organisational culture change (i.e. equipping people with the competency to make a difference).

Go MAD® can be used as a diagnostic tool to assess the current competence of individuals and teams; the probability of projects achieving success; and to identify areas for further action.

Go MAD® can be used as an analytical framework to identify why past decisions, projects and initiatives did not make the difference that was originally intended.

Day-to-day, the use of the Go MAD® process can be triggered by asking a couple of simple questions:

- "Am I bothered about this?"
- "Do I want to make a difference?"

If the answers are, "Yes," then skillful application of Go MAD® will help you make a difference.

Go MAD® - The art of making a difference

A book, "Go MAD - The Art of Making A Difference," was published following the research. Now, Go MAD® training and development programmes are being delivered worldwide as the Go MAD® process is increasingly being used by individuals and businesses who want to make a difference.

I have noticed, during the past couple of years, that a significant number of people who learn the Go MAD® process express a desire to one day write a book. I have also observed many people gaining enjoyment and inspiration from the many and varied quotations I use. So, for both these reasons, I decided to produce a book with a difference.

This book is designed for you to write in. Each page contains a quotation and a question. The quotations, selected from my ever-growing collection, will hopefully stimulate your mind and encourage you to make a difference. The questions have been designed to help you think about making that difference. They have been placed in a random order to trigger thoughts and ideas. I don't expect you to answer them all. Although, I am sure that you will gain significant benefit if you decide to do so!

Now it's time for you to decide what to write in your book. You might want to use it simply as a notebook or a personal development journal or possibly as something completely different. You decide - it's your book.

Read, write and make a difference.

Andy Gilbert

"The purpose of our lives is to be happy."
The 14th Dalai Lama

1

Q: What do you want to write this book about?

"Success lies in doing not what others consider to be great, but what you consider to be right." John Henry Gray

Q: What step can I take today to move towards what I want?

"In the middle of difficulty lies opportunity."
Albert Einstein

Q: What impact do I want to make?

"Neither fire nor wind, birth nor death can erase our good deeds." Buddha

Q: What changes have I been avoiding?

"There is nothing permanent except change."
Heraclitus

Q: What attributes do I possess?

"We are what we repeatedly do."
Aristotle

6

Q: How clear is my focus on the specific difference I want
to make?

"Words may show a man's wit, but actions his meaning."
Benjamin Franklin

Q: What is it possible for me to imagine in terms of my success?

"Success is for you, not others, to define."
Big Dan Trewler

Q: How strong is my desire?

"Kites rise highest against the wind - not with it."
Winston Churchill

Q: What makes me happy?

"Waste no tears over the griefs of yesterday."
Euripides

10

Q: What is the source of my reason for wanting to make a difference?

"If I have the belief that I can do it, I shall surely acquire the capacity to do it even if I may not have it at the beginning." Mahatma Gandhi

Q: How do I define success?

"Well done is better than well said."
Benjamin Franklin

Q: What gives me the greatest satisfaction?

"Self-belief is having as much confidence in yourself as you have in the people you most admire." Alan Smith

Q: How would I like others to describe me?

"The smallest difference is a million times better than indifference." Kathryn Roberts

Q: What are my priorities?

"Life shrinks or expands in proportion to one's own courage."
Anais Nin

Q: What do I like about myself?

"Nothing happens unless first a dream." Carl Sandburg

Q: Who do I enjoy spending time with?

"Accept what you cannot change; change what you cannot accept." Del Wrenibargt

Q: Who can I praise or encourage today?

"Behaviour breeds behaviour - if you make a difference others will follow." Euan Woodward

Q: What positive statement can I make about myself?

"I believe in life after birth."
Maxie Dunham

Q: Whose opinions do I respect and trust?

"If only we could stop saying "if only"."
Ian Chakravorty

Q: When am I going to start taking action?

"Imagination rules the world."
Napoleon

Q: How will I measure my progress?

"The time left is all we have got. It makes sense therefore to use it on the things we have prioritised as most important in our lives." Greta W. Brindle

Q: What am I going to do next?

"You see things and say, "why?" but I dream things that never were and say, "why not?"" George Bernard Shaw

Q: How will I thank others for helping me?

"A man has to live with himself, and he should see to it that he always has good company." Charles Hughes

24

Q: What legacy will I leave?

"The only person who decides whether you do or you don't is YOU!" Alison Lawrence

Q: How can I take greater personal responsibility for making it happen?

"Work to become, not to acquire."
Elbert Hubbard

Q: What makes life worth living?

"I will act as if what I do makes a difference."
William James

Q: How can I plan more effective use of my time?

"Do what you can with what you have, where you are."
Theodore Roosevelt

Q: What am I looking forward to?

"Make a difference - tell someone how special they are."
Nicky Frisby

Q: How much time do I spend doing the things I really want
to do?

"Choice, not chance, determines the differences you make."
Dr. W. Gart-Lieben

Q: What is the quality of my working relationship with colleagues?

"Nurture your minds with great thoughts. To believe in the heroic makes heroes." Benjamin Disraeli

Q: What makes me laugh?

"When you possess a passion or strong enough reason why, no-one else has to motivate you to make a difference."
Warren Digbelt

Q: What is my most empowering belief about my abilities?

"Never believe that NOW is the FUTURE!"
Grayson Newton

Q: What is my internal voice telling me to make a difference about?

"The focused mind can pierce through stone."
Japanese saying

Q: How much money do I need?

"If you don't have a good enough reason why to get out of bed, you might as well be asleep." Umang Panchal

Q: How can I create the right environment?

"You get what your mind predominantly focuses on. So feed it positive, successful thoughts." Debra W. Girlten

Q: Who do I want as friends?

"Mistakes are just steps on a journey to success."
Paul Roberts

Q: How can I build stronger relationships with people who are important to me?

"What we do is nothing but a drop in the ocean, but if we didn't do it, the ocean would be one drop less." Mother Teresa

Q: Which aspect of my job do I value most?

"Write down your goals - the worst ink survives the best memory." Harriett Gilbert

Q: Where do I want to go on holiday?

"You must be the change you wish to see in the world."
Mahatma Gandhi

40

Q: What is my ideal job?

"You can be the difference that makes a difference."
Gerrant Blewid

Q: How much time do I want to spend with my family?

"Whether you think you can or you can't - you are right."
Henry Ford

Q: What do I want to do this weekend?

"Our aspirations are our possibilities."
Robert Browning

Q: What has prevented me in the past from making a difference?

"There is no security in life, only opportunity."
Mark Twain

Q: How much do I want to weigh?

"People are like pots and pans - it is the recipe that makes a difference." Mary Parker

Q: What gives me hope?

"May you live all the days of your life."
Jonathan Swift

Q: Which places do I want to visit?

"Do you want to start, stop or stand still? It's your choice."
Dr. Li Wang Breet

Q: What luxury item would I like to buy myself?

"I dream for a living."
Steven Spielberg

Q: What dreams do I want to pursue?

"The future belongs to those who believe in the beauty of their dreams." Eleanor Roosevelt

Q: What ruts do I want to escape from?

"Your attitude is more important than your intellect."
Bridget Walner

Q: What possibilities do I need to consider?

"Your goal should be just out of reach, but not out of sight."
Denis Waitley & Reni L. Witt

Q: What specifically do I want to do, have, learn or become?

"Success is a science; if you have the conditions, you get the result." Oscar Wilde

Q: Who could possibly help me?

"Be not afraid of going slowly; be only afraid of standing still."
Chinese Proverb

Q: What resources do I need?

"Nothing is more powerful than an idea whose time has come."
Victor Hugo

Q: What can I do to increase my self-belief?

"Be ready to change, because change will happen."
Lt. Barnie Grewd

Q: How can I persuade others to help me make a difference?

"If it is to be, it is up to me."
Unknown

Q: What are my personal goals?

"Imagination is more powerful than knowledge, for knowledge is limited to all we know and understand, while imagination embraces the entire world, and all there ever will be to know and understand." Albert Einstein

Q: What qualities do I most admire in others?

"Let your imagination run wild; run with it and see where it takes you." Blair Grewdent

Q: How will I measure my success?

"The best time to plant a tree was twenty years ago. The second best time is now." Chinese proverb

Q: What do I aspire to?

"I will go anywhere as long as it is forward."
David Livingston

Q: What do I feel passionate about?

"Whistle while you work."
The Seven Dwarfs

Q: What single thing would make the greatest difference in my life?

"Making and keeping promises to ourselves precedes making promises and keeping promises to others." Steven R. Covey

Q: What makes me enthusiastic?

"It is not fair to ask of others what you are not willing to do yourself." Eleanor Roosevelt

Q: What needs to happen next?

"We think too small. Like the frog at the bottom of the well.
He thinks the sky is only as big as the top of the well. If he
surfaced, he would have an entirely different view."
Mao Tse-Tung

Q: How confident am I?

"Never look down on anyone, unless you're helping them up."
Rev. Jesse James

Q: How healthy is my lifestyle?

"You don't need to know anymore; you just need to apply more of what you already know." N.L. Waterbridge

Q: What skills do I need to develop?

"Don't let what you cannot do interfere with what you can do."
John Robert Wooden

Q: What subject would I enjoy learning about?

"Failure is an event, not a person."
Zig Ziglar

Q: How well balanced is my life?

"Good intentions mean nothing if they remain inside you."
Gina L. Tredbrew

Q: What financial goals do I have?

"The future belongs to those who prepare for it."
Ralph Waldo Emerson

Q: What do I want to become more confident about?

"What lies behind us and what lies before us are tiny matters compared to what lies within us." Oliver Wendell Holmes

Q: What fitness goals do I have?

"It is useless to desire more time if you are already wasting what little you have." James Allen

Q: What inspires me?

"Even if you are on the right track, you'll get run over if you just sit there." Will Rogers

Q: How relaxed am I?

"When a thought comes into your head, it's a possibility. If you reject the thought, then the possibility no longer exists."
Drew Bengaltir

Q: What do I want less of?

"It's not hard to make decisions when you know what your values are." Roy Disney

Q: What do I want more of?

"The greatest thing in this world is not so much where we are, but in which direction we are moving." Oliver Wendell Holmes

Q: Which direction am I moving in?

"No one is useless in this world who lightens the burden of another." Charles Dickens

Q: How important is the environment?

"The minute you begin to do what you want to do, it's really a different kind of life." Buckminster Fuller

Q: What can I contribute to others?

"If you can dream it, you can do it." Walt Disney

Q: How much personal responsibility am I taking for my career development?

"Always look ahead, it's better than looking at your behind."
Martin Saunders

Q: Which personal qualities would I benefit from developing?

"If you don't jump, you won't land." Unknown

Q: How many times do I complain about the weather?

"Happiness is a habit - cultivate it." Elbert Hubbard

Q: What is the state of my social life?

"The key to happiness is having dreams. The key to success is making dreams come true." Unknown

Q: What promise will I make to myself?

"And the trouble is, if you don't risk anything, you risk even more." Erica Long

Q: What do I contribute to my employer?

"The more doors you open the more you increase your probability of success." Mary Parker

Q: What can I say to keep myself going?

"I am still learning." Michelangelo

Q: When did I last compliment myself?

"Why focus on growing old? Why not keep your mind active and vow to die young, as late as possible!" Linda Bergwert

Q: How can I make a difference at work?

"Whatever the mind can conceive and believe, it can achieve."
Napoleon Hill

Q: How much do I like myself?

"The way I see it, if you want the rainbow, you gotta put up with the rain." Dolly Parton

Q: What leisure interests do I want to resume?

"A wise man creates more opportunities than he finds."
Francis Bacon

Q: How do I show others I love them?

"There is no such thing as a career path. It is crazy paving and you have to lay it yourself." Dominic Cadbury

Q: Who do I admire?

"The future belongs to people who see possibilities before they become obvious." Theodore Leavitt

Q: What sort of property do I want to live in?

"The most important relationship you will ever have is the relationship you have with yourself." Brian Weltgred

Q: How much T.V. do I really need to watch?

"Always bear in mind that your own resolution to succeed is more important than any other one thing." Abraham Lincoln

Q: How do I measure the success of my relationship?

"To succeed you have to believe in something with such a passion that it becomes reality." Anita Roddick

95

Q: What could bring more fun into my life?

"It is our attitude at the beginning of a difficult undertaking which more than anything else, will determine its successful outcome." William James

Q: Who do I want to work with?

"Quality is remembered long after the price is forgotten."
Gucci family slogan

Q: What gives me that "feel good" factor?

"Just Do It."
Nike advertising slogan

Q: How many of my fears are imagined?

"Before anything else, getting ready is the secret of success."
Henry Ford

Q: What possibilities do I see?

"If I really want to improve my situation, I can work on the one thing over which I have control - myself." Steven R. Covey

100

Q: What do I want to learn to live with?

"If you wait until the wind and the weather are just right, you will never plant anything and never harvest anything."
Ecclesiastes 11:4

Q: What would increase team spirit?

"Life is no brief candle, but a splendid torch."
George Bernard Shaw

Q: Which mental blocks do I want to overcome?

"Some men have thousands of reasons why they cannot do what they want to, when all they need is one reason they can."
Willis R. Whitney

Q: What do I want to be more tolerant of?

"We make a living by what we get, but we make a life by what we give." Norman MacEswan

Q: How can I help my partner?

"Life is either a daring adventure or nothing."
Helen Keller

Q: What would I love to celebrate?

"Without vision the people perish." Proverbs 29:18

Q: What have I been procrastinating about?

"It is not the mountain we conquer, but ourselves."
Sir Edmund Hillary

Q: Am I moving towards something or away from something?

"Determine your own pass criteria. Treat life like an exam where you get the opportunity to set the pass mark!"
Darren Gelbwit

Q: What will ensure my success?

"It's either right or it's wrong and you'll know the difference."
Charlie Haggie

Q: How can I reduce the level of pressure on myself?

"Life's most urgent question is, what are you doing for others?" Martin Luther King, Jr.

Q: What does completion look like?

"We don't see things as they are, we see things as we are."
Anais Nin

Q: What is the quality of my closest relationship?

"A candle loses nothing by lighting another candle."
Unknown

Q: How can I make more opportunities for myself?

"The mind is the greatest power in all of creation."
J.B. Rhine

Q: What is my purpose in life?

"You're a grown up - you can do what you want!"
Peter Thomson

Q: Who else would I like to write a book?

"In times of change the learners will inherit the earth, while the learned find themselves beautifully equipped to deal with a world that no longer exists." Eric Hoffer

Q: What are my core values?

"I will not let anyone walk through my mind with their dirty feet." Mahatma Gandhi

Q: What could I do differently today?

"Go MAD® is more than "Go-getting." It involves the concept of "Go-giving"." Andy Gilbert

Q: Which friend can I most easily help to make a difference?

Contact the Go MAD® Team...

If you would like to receive more information about other books in the Go MAD® range or details of other Go MAD® personal and business development products.

OR

If you are looking for new, inspiring, practical ways to develop yourself or your organisation, we offer a range of innovative Go MAD® training solutions, conference speakers, personal coaches and consultancy options.

Go MAD Ltd
Pocket Gate Farm
Off Breakback Road
Woodhouse Eaves
Leicestershire
LE12 8RS

01509 891313

www.gomadonline.com

info@gomadonline.com

If you liked this book and would like to be kept advised of other Go MAD® books please let us know.

Other Go MAD® book titles include:

Go MAD - The Art of Making A Difference

Go MAD about Coaching - Coaching Made Easy

Go MAD about Meetings - 87 Ways to Make A Difference

59 Minutes to a Calmer Life

Go to Work on Your Career

Contagious Customer Care

If you would like to receive free inspirational quotes on a weekly basis or involve others in helping you to make a difference, visit the website:

www.principlefive.com

If you would like to receive information about the Go MAD® monthly audio magazine and discover how it can further develop your ability to make a difference, visit the website:

www.gomadonline.com